The Enchanting Fairies Colouring Book

The Enchanting Fairies Colouring Book

Beautiful fairies to colour and complete

ARCTURUS

ARCTURUS

This edition published in 2017 by Arcturus Publishing Limited
26/27 Bickels Yard, 151–153 Bermondsey Street,
London SE1 3HA

Design copyright © Arcturus Holdings Limited

All illustrations © the Medici Society/Mary Evans Picture Library

Black and white artwork by Peter Gray

ISBN: 978-1-78428-408-4
CH005409NT
Supplier 36, Date 0217, Print Run 6105

Printed in Italy

Created for children 10+

Introduction

This colouring book explores the wonderful imagination of Margaret Tarrant, a book and greetings card illustrator who was at her most prolific during the 1920s and 1930s. Here, Tarrant's full-colour images are paired with line drawings for you to work on, either by following the artist's choice of colours or by choosing a palette of your own.

Margaret Tarrant was born in Battersea, a suburb of south London, on 19 August 1888, the only child of Sarah Wyatt and the painter and illustrator Percy Tarrant, who encouraged her early artistic talents. As a child, Margaret would set up an 'Exhibition Tent' with sheets, then pin up her artwork and invite her parents inside for a viewing. In 1905 she began to train as an art teacher, but a lack of confidence in her ability to teach led her father to guide her into his own profession of illustrator.

At the age of eighteen, Tarrant began to work for publishers of Christmas cards, and developed her talents through many and varied commissions. Soon after the family's move to Gomshall, Surrey, she illustrated her first book, a new edition of Charles Kingsley's *The Water Babies* (1908). From this point on, she applied her creativity and skill as a figure artist to chronicling aspects of childhood, particularly imaginative play.

After becoming established as an illustrator, Margaret studied at Heatherley's School of Art, in London, and then at Guildford School of Art, where she met fellow artist Molly Brett. She also exhibited at the Royal Academy between 1914 and 1927, and at the Royal Birmingham Society of Artists. In 1920, she began her most important business relationship, with the Medici Society. Her work for this company ranged from books to posters and calendars and gave her wide exposure and huge popularity. Though her approach may seem highly idealized, even romanticized, its success lies in the degree to which it is grounded in close observation and the discipline of drawing from life. The Medici Society still publishes her books, cards and calendars today.

Tarrant worked in many media, including pen-and-ink, watercolour and graphite. According to a mother whose child Margaret had sketched, she would start various drawings as the child moved around, sketching an arm here, a leg there, returning to the sketch as the child resumed position again. She would then invent her composition, adapting the figures from the series of sketches.

The delightful depictions of fairies and flowers in these pages amply demonstrate Tarrant's gift as an open-hearted artist of skill and sensitivity.

Catch it if you can

Tulip fairies

Margaret W. Tarrant

Autumn dancer

Larkspur and red admiral

Wood anemone or windflower

Harvest festival

Ladies' slipper

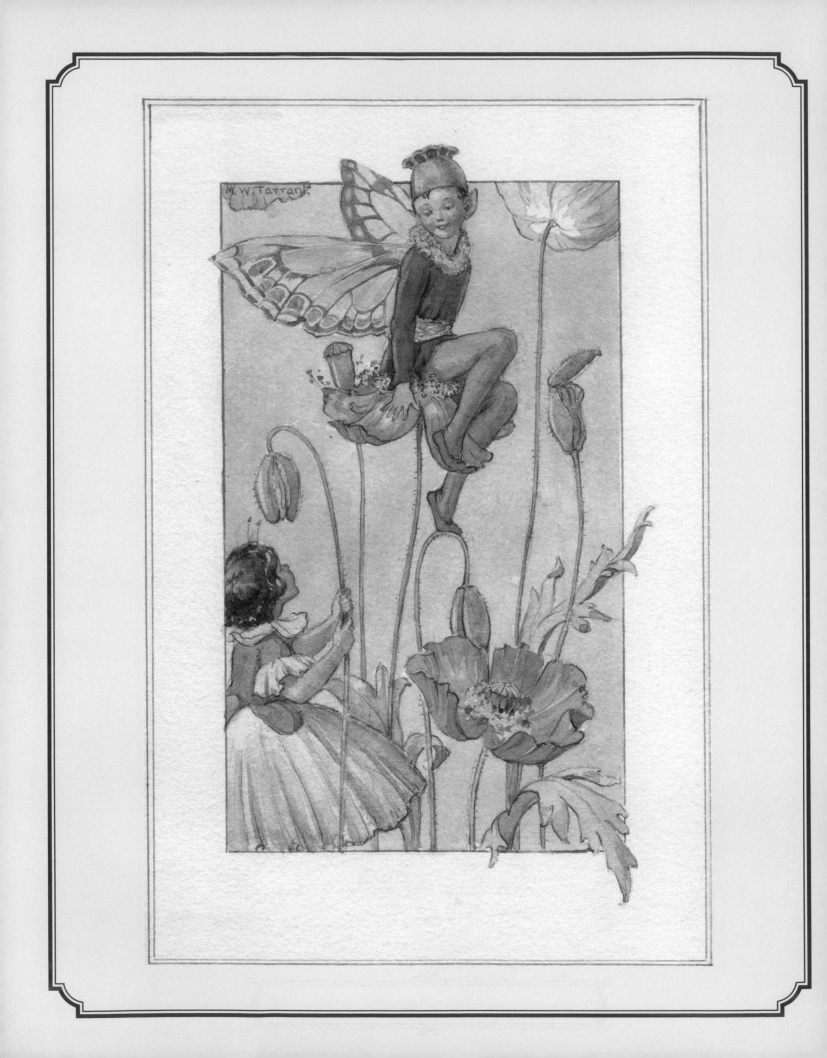

Poppy fairies

Hazel catkins

Toadstool painters

Harebell ringer

Citrus songstress

Man overboard!

Winter's chill

Pond chase

Margaret W. Tarrant

Dragonfly ride

Wild raspberries

Margaret W. Tarrant

Blueberry fairy

Spring is here!

Swim for your life!

Mouse music

Margaret W. Tarrant

Rose petal bedtime

Nocturnal raid

Waterlily fairies

Cherry fairy

Margaret W Tarrant

Crab apples

Apple blossom

Pear blossom and orange tips

Chinese lantern fairies

Spindleberry fairies

Margaret W. Tarrant.

Dandelion fairies

Sycamore spinners

Blissful innocence

Snowfall fairies

Jack Frost

Mist

The Winds

Sunshine

Sweet clover

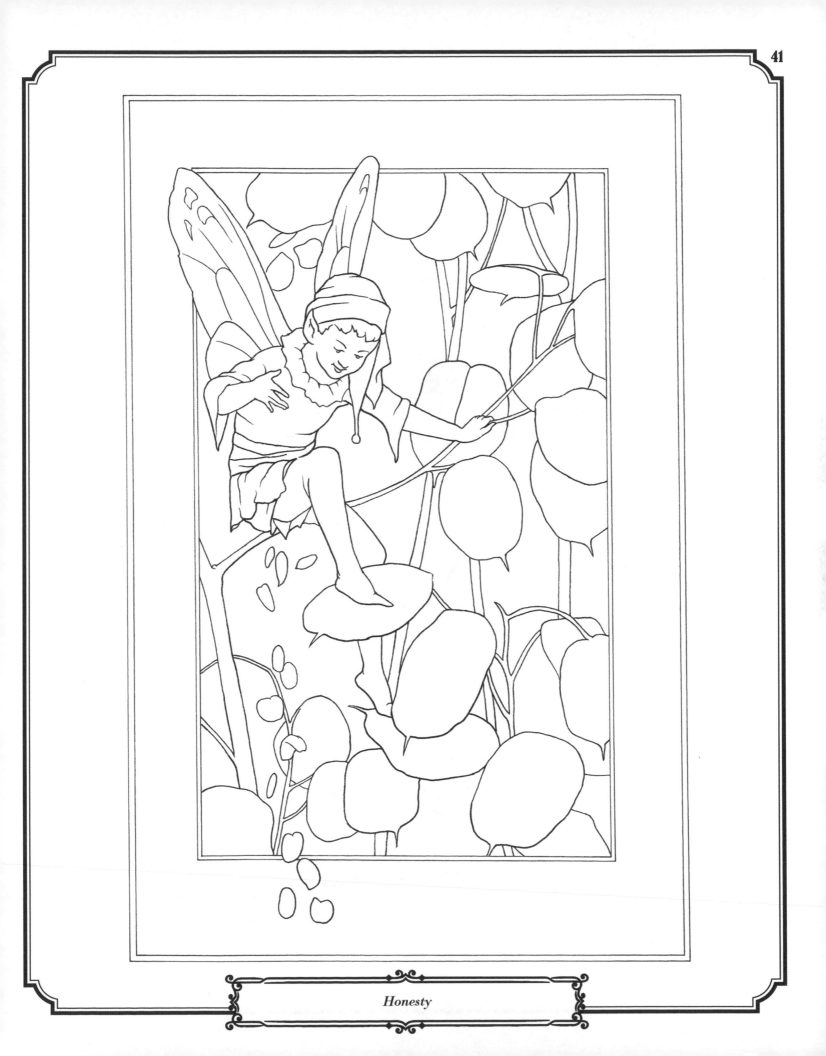

Honesty

Starlight

Sweet peas

Little Snowdrop

Moonlight vigil